GENESIS GIRLS

– BOOK ONE –

EVE
BELIEVED

Eve Believed
Eve Believed
By Paige Henderson
Copyright ©2017

Contact: paige.henderson@fellowshipofthesword.com
All rights reserved.

Henderson House Publishing

Cover design by Kolton Rogers
Original Artwork (eyes): Look at Me by Kendra Ward

The Genesis Girls Series is dedicated to...

My parents, Larry & Rachel, for dedicating me to the Lord and meaning it. Look what that dedication did!

My husband, Richard, for agitating my creativity and propping up my confidence. These Girls have voices because yours is so loud.

My sons, Riley and Maddox (Gus and Buzz), who inspire me to go adventuring. Hey, y'all! Watch this!

My sisters, Leanne & Jennifer, for sharing the backseat of my life – breathing my air, touching my stuff, crossing my lines, and reminding me that, in the end, we are all just real girls.

The "Crack'd Pots" of Vail, Colorado who got me started on this whole Genesis Girl adventure. You know who you are!

Brian and Sabrina who took what I had and squeezed the Life out of it.

Sally who heard the Girls when they were "just" words and listened.

For those who've ever felt disqualified

TABLE OF CONTENTS

I would have despaired,

unless I had believed I would see

the goodness of Yahweh

in the land of the living.

Psalm 27:13

FOREWORD

I am a church girl through and through. In truth, I was a church girl before I was born because my mother registered me in the nursery in January before I was born in May. That's how much a church girl I am. If it were possible to have "church girl" on one of your DNA markers, it would be on mine. As an in utero church member I was destined to grow up loving the Bible and all its wonderful stories. Some of my earliest memories are of the people I met in the pages of my Bible primer in Sunday school.

Until a few years ago, those Sunday school stories were all I knew of the women whose lives form the very bedrock of my beliefs. I call them the *Genesis Girls* because their stories all are contained in the first book of our Bible. These are the first women and their stories are our inheritance. They are the answer to the question of where we come from as women. Their interactions with the freshly created world, their indentations in the clay of the new story of Man's Relationship to God matter deeply to understanding "a woman's place" in the Kingdom.

Even though these women are fundamental to my Christian faith, I had never spent any time getting to know them. I did know some facts about some of them:

- Eve—first woman, disobeyed God, all mankind suffers because of her, wore fig leaves.

- Sarah—got in trouble because she laughed when God said she'd have a child.

- Rachel—the pretty one.

That was about all I could tell you about the women from whom my very existence flows and upon whom my spiritual heritage is built. I started digging into the *Genesis Girls* because as a woman I knew there had to be more to their stories than the shallow *Sunday School Digest* version.

As I went back to my Bible and re-read their stories something wonderful happened. The Lord suddenly breathed life into them, and my black and white *Genesis Girl* paper dolls came up off the pages in high-definition, three-dimensional living color. They walked and talked and laughed and cried and loved and hurt and mourned and rejoiced. They were real women, not just so many handfuls of recorded facts.

These women became my mentors and friends. No, we don't meet for lunch at quaint sidewalk cafes or have long heartfelt conversations as we walk through autumn leaves, but I've found comfort, wisdom, hope, and so much more in their stories. My prayer is you will too.

All of that being said, I'm going to turn the pages over to the one who started it all. It's all yours, Eve.

INTRODUCTION
I'M *THAT* EVE

Thank you, Paige.

Hi, I'm Eve. Yes, *that* Eve, the one your mothers and Sunday school teachers told you about, no doubt with many warnings not to follow in my footsteps. It's right here on my nametag: First name, Eve, last name, Responsible For The Fall of Mankind. That's me.

You probably believe my story is some version of "The Creator said not to, she did, He chased her out of the Garden, and all mankind still suffers because of what Eve did." End of story. There I stand, half-naked outside the Garden for all eternity. Right?

Wrong.

Yes, I did disobey Elohim, and yes, all mankind has had to pay for my mistake, but that's just one chapter. Seriously, that is just Chapter 3 of your Bible's book of Genesis. There was more before that and so much more after, although you have to dig deeper to get to know me better.

Having heard my story mis-told more than a few times, I've learned the best thing is to dispense with all the Bible-speak and tell my story in my own words so we can go deeper. There was no Bible-speak in the Garden because there was no Bible. I wasn't reading this story. I was living it, so trust me to get it right, even if the words I use are not what you're used to reading.

I know you've heard of my infamous encounter with the serpent and the fruit, but I want you to hear my *whole* story because I think you'll find it's your story too. Well, okay, not the fall of mankind part, but my story is about being a wife, a mother, about love, joy and unimaginable heartache, about mistakes—big ones—and redemption, and about believing in and living the kind of abundant life Elohim designed for all. It's also about creating. Not just creating other humans, but creating an environment of obedience and perseverance where life flourishes.

Once you hear the whole story, I believe you'll change your mind about me and hopefully want to follow in my footsteps, at least on the path *outside* the Garden. You may rethink what you believe about our Creator as well.

So, let's start at the beginning.

FIRST THINGS

The beginning is Elohim. I'm not trying to sound "theological" (I don't really even know what that means), but He's the beginning of my story because He is *the* beginning. You know Him by other names— Lord, God, Father, Jehovah, Jesus, Savior, Comforter, such a long list—but His original name, the one I first knew and the first one in your Bible is Elohim.

I love calling Him Elohim. It may seem strange and impersonal to you, but every time I speak that name I am reminded that He is my sovereign, majestic, exalted Creator, the One that made this incredible world and filled it with His goodness. In your Bible, He is Elohim throughout your book of Genesis: "In the beginning, Elohim." That's my Elohim. Everywhere in your book of Genesis that you read "God" I hear "Elohim."

I came to know Him also as Yahweh, the personal, loving, faithful One who breathed life into us: "And the LORD God [Yahweh-Elohim] formed man of the dust of the ground, and breathed into his nostrils the breath of life; and man became a living being" (Gen.

2:7 NKJV). Everywhere in Genesis you see the words "the LORD," that's the name Yahweh.

I call Him both because I know Him as my sovereign Creator and faithful Life-Giver. I hope you learn to love these names as much as I do. If you don't yet know Him as *your* Elohim or as Yahweh, I hope before my story is over you want to.

THERE I AM

Ah, yes, the beginning. I remember like it was yesterday, and every time I do my heart pounds with joy and excitement. Picture this if you can: It's the sixth day of creation; there are blooming flowers, thick foliage, fur-covered animals, and colorful birds *everywhere.* The Earth is teeming with life and beauty. Elohim has just finished creating Adam and me to be just like Him, and then He blesses us and speaks the first words ever uttered to humanity—oh, hold on. If a question mark popped up in your mind when I made that statement about being created on Day Six, let me assure you, I was there, but I also understand you may not have heard my story as starting there.

The account of my formation seems more specifically told in Genesis Chapter 2 of your Bible, but as with so much of my story, you have to delve a bit deeper to understand more fully. I was created on the sixth day with Adam. You don't see me or hear my name on Day

Six, but trust me, I was there, tucked away inside Adam until the time was right for Yahweh to reveal me.

Neither Adam nor any of the rest of creation saw me at my instant of conception, but Elohim did. I was conceived in His mind and in His words simultaneously with Adam and created at the instant the thought was formed. Elohim is The Creator. Everything that exists, seen and unseen, began in His mind, with His intent, and because He lives in timeless eternity, there's no chronology. It all is as He thinks it. The second He intends something, it is, regardless of whether the physical manifestation of it is present.

If you've read Genesis 1:27 in your Bible, you've read about my creation on the sixth day, although you may not have *seen* me: "So Elohim created mankind in his own image, in the image of Elohim He created them; male and female He created them" (Gen. 1:27). There I am. Do you see me? That's me, the female part of "them" Elohim made on Day Six.

GET CHOCOLATE IN YOUR EYEBROWS!

I was there, and I heard His voice as He spoke His love to us: "Be fruitful! Multiply! Fill the Earth! Subdue it! Reign!" (Gen. 1:28). I'd never heard any word before. This is literally the first thing my mind comprehended at the instant of my creation. Wow! From the beginning, Elohim's love and goodness saturated my mind in those spoken words: "Be fruitful! Multiply! Fill! Subdue! Reign!"

If you're not as excited as I am about those words, it's probably because you and I aren't interpreting them exactly the same. Our Creator wasn't telling Adam and me just to go have a lot of babies. I think there's been a lot of that idea promulgated since Day Six. I mean, it was definitely part of the whole fruitful assignment and there definitely was some multiplying that occurred, but that word "fruitful" actually means to flourish.

Flourish, in your dictionary, means "to be strong and healthy or grow well, *especially because conditions are right*." I can testify the conditions were more than "right." Elohim had created an environment that was perfect for me and Adam to flourish forever.

When I heard those words, I heard my Elohim inviting me into His wonderful creation: "Come see what I've made for you! Enjoy it! Have a great time! Suck it all in! Love it! Thrive in it! Oh, and then go make more of yourselves so you can show them what I've made and teach them to flourish as well!"

This was a party, and it was all for us! But not just for us: for everyone that would follow us! Our assignment was to joyfully charge into the perfect, beautiful paradise Elohim made, experience every good and wonderful thing He'd put there, and then make more of ourselves so they could do the same thing…forever!

If you like to lick the chocolate cake batter off the beaters of a mixer (I know you do), Elohim was handing us the beaters, the wooden spoon, the plastic spatula, and the bowl and saying "Here! It's all yours! Lick them clean! Dive in head first and don't come up until you have chocolate in your eyebrows!" Yes, that was my first assignment: Go get chocolate in your eyebrows. And I did!

Sounds like heaven on earth, doesn't it? It was.

YOU NEED A RIB

From the beginning I was there, doing exactly what I was designed to do, the same things you are designed to do: creating an environment that supports and protects life. I was created with Adam, but formed from his rib, an important distinction I think you'll come to understand.

Being formed from one of Adam's ribs is another of those things I get really excited about, but seems to lose its impact when I speak to others about it. I guess it may have to do with my more personal understanding of how amazing ribs are, being a little less removed from them than you. Ribs have unique characteristics and once you know more about them, you'll understand how special it is to be formed from them.

We really should talk about the symbolism of Elohim forming me from Adam's rib and not part of his skull or his little toe bone. Adam needed a helper, not a boss or a door mat. When you need help, you don't look for someone who's just going to tell you all the things you need to do but is too exalted in their own eyes to get their hands dirty. You also don't need someone weaker than you or someone you can trample on. You need help, and that means someone at least as strong as you who will jump in and work *alongside* you. You need a rib.

STRENGTH AND STRATEGY

While we're talking about helping, your Bible tells you Yahweh made Adam a "helpmeet," which sounds sort of odd in your language so most people simple say I was Adam's helper. Not that I want to get too hung up on words, but seriously, the word "helper" doesn't really convey all that Yahweh designed me—I mean, us to be.

What my Elohim actually said just before He took me from Adam's side was Adam needed an *ezer k'enegdo*[1]. It's two words that when combined mean something a lot more than a helper. We'll talk about *k'enegdo* later. For now, let's look at *ezer*. *Ezer* is the word used for military help. It's not "Help me finish the laundry" or "I've got better things to do. It would sure help if you'd make me a pot of coffee so in a minute when I take a break from all this important stuff I'm doing, I can drink the coffee you made." Not even close.

That's not the kind of help Adam needed and not the kind of help Yahweh created me—created us to provide. It's help as in "I have just fought all day to take this piece of ground from the enemy, and I need somebody to hold it for me so I can go rest half a second and come back to my job." *Ezer* is help that builds up, unifies, and shields. That's the strength and strategy kind of help Yahweh designed when He formed me from Adam's rib.

ARCHITECTURAL WONDER

Now to the other things I want to share with you about ribs you may not know. First of all, the anatomical structure of the human body places ribs around the most vital organs, the heart and lungs, to protect them from outside harm. Yes, women have been protecting life since before we were called "women."

If the rib cage were of manmade construction, it would be sort of an architectural wonder. The 24 ribs, the sternum, 12 thoracic vertebrae, and costal cartilages work together to make the rib cage one of the strongest yet most delicate structures in the human body. Its strength comes from the unique way the somewhat fragile, curved bones fit perfectly together to be firm and at the same time remain flexible because of the elastic costal cartilage that connects them. You were created to be strong but not rigid; to be flexible but also firm.

Further, ribs are essential for you to breathe. When you

take a breath, your diaphragm contracts and pulls the rib cage downward. It's this downward motion that actually sucks air into your lungs. Conversely, when the diaphragm releases, air is pushed out of the lungs by the rib cage. If ribs become severely damaged they stop working with the diaphragm and you can't breathe. You know what happens if you can't breathe.

ADAM DIDN'T LOSE ANYTHING

Next, ribs are one of the only bones in the human body that continue to produce red blood marrow, and therefore red blood cells, into adulthood. They continually replenish the body's blood supply, making ribs, once again, essential to sustaining life. And the last thing—and I think this is the one that sort of puts me in awe the most—is that ribs are the only bones in the body that regenerate.

It's true. One reason ribs are used so often in bone grafts by your surgeons is if the outer covering of the rib bone is left intact when the inner bone material is removed, a new bone grows back. This isn't the same as other bones that have the capacity to heal themselves (which shouldn't be overlooked as rather amazing as well). This is an actual brand-new bone growing after the *complete* removal of its predecessor.

Before the study of human anatomy, some assumed men had one less rib than women because of my being formed from one of Adam's. Of course, that idea went right out the window as soon as doctors began to study human skeletons. Sure, Adam gave up a rib so I could be revealed, but it grew back. Yahweh planned it that way.

Adam didn't lose anything so I could take my place beside him any more than I am less than him because my name is mentioned second in your Bible. I wasn't an afterthought when Adam couldn't find an *ezer k'enegdo*. My Elohim didn't look around and say, "Oh, no! What have I done? I forgot something. Shoot! Now what?" I was always there, coexisting with and completely equal to Adam in every way, just as Elohim designed me; just as He designed you.

MADE FOR EACH OTHER

I remember the moment Yahweh revealed me to Adam after He'd fashioned me from his rib. I wish you could have heard the thrill in his voice as he said those eight little words that still send chills up my spine: "Bone of my bones! Flesh of my flesh!" Did you feel that? No chills? Okay, maybe it's the age difference.

Anyway, there he was calling me the flesh of his flesh, and I knew it was on like green on grass on Day Three in the Garden of Eden. He knew it too. He recognized me instantly as the one for him. We were made for each other—literally—which brings me to the rest of Yahweh's description of us.

The word *k'enegdo*, which has been translated "meet" or "suitable," is used only two times in your entire Bible, in Genesis 2:18 and 20, both times when referring to the companion Elohim would make for Adam. Its root word, *neged*, is used elsewhere and usually means "against," "toward," or "opposite." That definition is not very helpful in understanding Yahweh's explanation of the role women play in concert with men—until you look a little deeper.

Look at your hands, the left and the right. They are exactly alike and completely different, all at the same time. Same with your feet. Can you imagine trying to work with two right hands or walk with two left feet? When you look in a mirror, you see your exact image only the exact opposite. That's what Yahweh was saying as He pronounced His design of the relationship between me and Adam and between men and women for all time.

IDENTICAL OPPOSITES

Hold your hands in front of you and then clasp them together, fingers intertwined. That's the picture of how men and women are to fit and work perfectly together: Identical opposites. We are strong, strategic, exactly equal, exactly the same, and completely different from men, just as Yahweh declared.

When Yahweh pulled back the curtain and revealed me

("Ta-da!"), Adam looked at me and exclaimed, "My bone! My flesh!" Adam instantly recognized me and valued me as his worthy partner, and I him as mine. Adam wasn't just announcing that I was perfect and exactly what he wanted. I was, but he was the same for me.

Adam's exclamation was much more than that. It was recognition of the appearance of what Yahweh decreed just *before* He created us: "Let us make mankind in our image, in our likeness, so that they may rule over the fish in the sea and the birds in the sky, over the livestock and all the wild animals, and over all the creatures that move along the ground."[2]

Adam and I *together* are the "they" Elohim created to rule over the earth. I was revealed as the completion of the physical expression of Yahweh's word when He declared *us* made in His image. Adam was They Part 1, I was They Part 2, and together *we* completed the image of Yahweh in the earth.

Adam was declaring, "Here's the rest of the Image!" He was agreeing with Yahweh, and welcoming me into the relationship as a worthy partner. I was seen and valued.

With his words, Adam anointed me into my purpose, as if the place at the table had been set and he'd been waiting for me to arrive. He didn't turn to Yahweh and ask, "What's this, another creature to name?" because he already knew. He called me *ishah* (Gen. 2:23). Your Bible transliterates Adam's name for me as "woman," but just as there's more to Yahweh's description of us as *ezer k'enegdo* than "helper," there's more to *ishah*.

Before there were letters for written language, there were pictographs, drawings that represented words, phrases, or even ideas. The pictographs that evolved into the Hebrew word *ishah,* which has been translated into your word "woman," speaks to a perspective difference that results in discernment and wisdom. By calling me *ishah* Adam declared and confirmed men and women literally see things differently. At my very core—and at yours—is a perspective of wisdom and discernment different than any man's.

With my name, Adam affirmed he recognized I was part of him, exactly the same but completely different from him in form and perspective, and the one who would walk by his side to build, to protect, to unify, and to sustain life in all that lay ahead. Yes, those were some good days in the Garden, just me and Adam and Yahweh. I have no idea how long that season lasted— no one was counting time in the Garden—but I know it was too short.

Now before you get all "Oh, here she goes. It's going to get gloomy," let me stop you. Gloomy I am not!

Not that I haven't passed through some gloomy times, but I promise "gloomy" is not my story any more than making clothes from fig leaves and running out of the Garden of Eden half-naked. If that's what you think, you're in for a great surprise.

Nevertheless, I guess we do have to talk about the serpent in the room, so here goes.

THE SUPREME
STUPIDITY

I don't care who you are, nobody wants to be remembered for their greatest stupidity. I mean, do you want your legacy to be the dumbest thing you ever did? Neither do I. Sadly, the only thing most know about me is my infamous meeting with "the serpent" and "eating the fruit." Though not something I like to spend a great deal of time talking about, it is part of my story, and since I promised you the whole story, this is what happened.

After Yahweh told us to go celebrate life, He told us one more thing: "Eat up! There are thousands of plants and trees in the Garden with good fruit for you. Enjoy! There's only one tree out there I want you to steer clear of. It's the Tree of the Knowledge of Good and Evil. Do NOT eat that fruit! It will kill you!" (Gen. 2:16–17). I know that's probably not exactly how you've read it, but that's how I remember Him telling me and Adam about The Fruit.

THE VOICES YOU HEED
Elohim, Adam, and I spent a great deal of time talking,

especially in the evenings when He'd come walk in the Garden with us. The only two voices I'd ever heard were Adam's and Elohim's because there were no other voices in the Garden—until I moved a little too close to The Tree. To hear another voice was startling; to hear what it said even more so. Elohim said the fruit would kill us. Suddenly there's another voice telling me it won't.

Let's stop right here and let me ask a question. How many voices are you listening to? In your world, there are hundreds of voices every day telling you how to live and what to believe. Think about it. You are bombarded with voices that tell you how to dress, how to make money, how to raise your children, how to treat people, how to find a mate, how to keep a mate, how to wear your hair, how to clean your house, what to eat—I guess that brings us full circle.

My first stupidity (not my greatest) was choosing to listen to a foreign voice. This wasn't the voice of someone close to me who loved me. This was a voice I'd never heard, and yet, I chose to hear it and heed it.

The ability to choose is both empowering and terrifying because choices decide your destiny; in many cases, the destiny of others; in at least one case, the destiny of mankind. The voice I chose to hear that day in the Garden was not my Elohim's. I knew His voice; it was kind and sure, strong and life-giving. The comfort and sweetness of His voice filled me with deep peace. It vibrated with love and adoration.

The serpent's voice slithered across my ears. It was mocking and contemptuous as it challenged me about Yahweh's command against eating from the Tree of Knowledge. Still, I listened. It was accusing and reproachful as it contradicted Elohim's declaration of death and cast aspersions on His truthfulness. Still, I listened. It was strong-arming and intimidating as it promised more wisdom, more autonomy, more discernment. Still, I listened.

As I listened, the serpent's voice drew my attention away from all the beauty of every other tree and every other fruit in the Garden. I looked away from the abundance of goodness Yahweh had given and fixed my eyes on the one thing I shouldn't have. I found myself fixated on the fruit Yahweh had forbidden. I had listened too long to the serpent.

The longer I gazed at the fruit, the more appetizing it became. Its color was brilliant and shiny. I imagined its juice would be as sweet as its skin was beautiful. Not only was it beautiful, its very name offered the promise of wisdom, which is something I surely should have more of. After all, discernment and wisdom were part of my name, my purpose, my identity. Yes, Elohim would *definitely* want me to have more wisdom. All I have to do, then, is eat this fruit and I will be wiser, have more discernment, and no doubt be a better *ezer k'enegdo* to Adam. This fruit will be good for me! It will be good for us! One piece probably won't be enough.

Enter my supreme stupidity: I ate it. Not only that, when I didn't fall down dead, I gave it to Adam. "Listen, I had a bite and I'm still here. I think it's okay." Adam saw the fruit looked good and I hadn't dropped like a rock, so he took a bite.

EYES WIDE OPEN

Before he could finish swallowing, our whole world disappeared. Really disappeared. Neither of us could see the world we'd seen only a blink before. It was gone, just like that, in the breaking of the skin of that piece of fruit. What was left in its place, though not completely unfamiliar was completely different.

Your Bible tells you at that moment Adam and I realized we were naked. Actually, we knew we were unclothed before then. We'd felt the cool breeze on our skin as we walked in the evenings with Elohim. We'd felt the warmth of the sun as we daily flourished in the Garden. The moment we laid eyes on each other, we knew we were naked.[3]

The nakedness we suddenly perceived was more than realizing we weren't wearing any clothing. The moment we ate the fruit, the eyes of our hearts snapped closed and the eyes of our flesh flew wide open. Until that moment, we saw all of creation, all of our existence through spiritual eyes, just as Elohim because we were made in His image. When the substance of your life is spirit, flesh is your clothing, but when the substance of your life is flesh, you have nothing.

We were uncovered, totally exposed. This wasn't an instantaneous revelation of some sort of modesty. This was an instantaneous revelation that we had sinned, and we were desperate to conceal what we'd done.

FIG-LEAF FASHION

I've come to understand what we were feeling right then you call shame. I'd never imagined such a feeling so certainly didn't know it had a name. All we could think about was finding a way to hide because, as I'm sure you know, sin begs to be covered up. We grabbed some large fig leaves and began to piece them together. They were awful but in our desperation to cover up what we'd done, we put them on. It didn't work. We still felt exposed so we stayed in the bushes, trying to conceal our sin.

Then I felt something else I'd never felt before. It was fear. I was suddenly filled with fear that Yahweh would know what we'd done. The fear forced us deeper and deeper into the foliage, for the first time not running out to meet Him for our evening walk through the Garden.

A moment later we heard Him walking in the Garden. He was coming, calling Adam's name. He was going to see the hideous fig-leaf swimming suits we'd pieced together. What would we say? And then He was there in our midst…but we could not see Him. I turned my head every direction. I strained my eyes open wider and wider. I could not see Him.

Another wave of emotion I'd never felt, this one worse than the shame and fear of before: Regret. I could no longer see my majestic, exalted Elohim, whose indescribable glory I had once seen and walked with as we talked together. My heart felt as though it would burst. I couldn't catch my breath. Suddenly water was flowing out of my eyes, my stomach churned and I was breathing uncontrollably as horrible sounds came from my chest.

WAITING TO DIE

At that moment, although I had no idea what death was, I almost hoped it would happen so the horror I was caught in would end. I was completely exposed and utterly defenseless, I was terrified to the point of hysterics , and the One I loved, whom every part of my heart and mind longed to see and commune with, my Creator, my Breath of Life, my Elohim, my Yahweh was gone from my sight. Forever. I waited to die.

But I didn't.

Instead I heard Elohim speaking to Adam. If you've read this conversation and imagined the voice of Elohim angry, you couldn't be more wrong. His words were firm but soothing:

"Where are you?"

"I heard Your voice and I was afraid because I'm naked, so I hid."

"Oh, Adam, who told you you were naked? I didn't teach you that word. Have you eaten from the tree that I told you not to touch?"

"The woman gave me the fruit, and I ate it."

Then He was speaking to me in the same manner:

"What have you done?"

"The serpent deceived me, and I ate it."

LET THE HEALING BEGIN

You know as well as I the all-powerful, all-knowing, Supreme Creator of all that has ever been, is, or will be knew where we were. And what we'd done. He wasn't asking because He needed the information. He wasn't walking around in the bushes, "Gee, I wonder where Adam and Eve are and what they've been up to today."

He wasn't trying to catch us in a lie, accuse us, or make us feel bad. He wasn't looking for a reason to punish us. In His goodness and because of His incalculable love for us, He was giving us the opportunity to confess our sin so He could heal us! There's no healing without acknowledging. It's a spiritual principle you can read about in your Bible (James 5:16). I couldn't. I was learning all this as it was happening.

The next words Elohim spoke were to the serpent—and *only* the serpent. That's an important distinction. In your Bible you see the word "cursed," several sentences directed at the serpent (Gen. 3:14–15), and then Elohim begins to speak to me (v. 16). It's easy to read those sentences, misunderstand, and think His words to me and Adam were part of a curse. I assure you, they were not.

In fact, Elohim's final words to the serpent were to reveal that deceiver's ultimate destruction and our ultimate redemption. Though directed at the serpent, these beautiful words of hope revealed Elohim's plan of salvation for Adam and I—and you—to hear:

> *"And I will put enmity between you and the woman, and between your offspring and hers; He will crush your head, and you will strike His heel."*[4]

The promise that One would someday come through me to utterly destroy the serpent was a sunburst in the midnight of my heart. My Elohim did not leave me hopeless!

A LIFE OF FLESH

Elohim never cursed Adam or me, and He wasn't raging at us for our disobedience. I was there, and I can tell you unequivocally the emotion I heard in His voice was never anger. Never. At the time, I didn't have a name for the feeling I heard in His voice as He spoke. My emotional repertoire, although expanding rapidly, was still limited. There would be a time, however, when I would know firsthand what my Elohim was feeling as He prepared us for what was ahead. That part of my story is yet to come.

As the serpent slipped away under the grass, Elohim told Adam and me what a life of flesh would be like:

"Eve, without me, you're going to want to take all that strength and passion I formed in you, and you're going to want to be in control with it. But just as I didn't make you to be the tail, I also didn't make you to be the head. You will strive to be in that position, but you will never be satisfied in it. To fix that, you're going to need Me."

"Adam, without me, you're going to think you are

the sole responsible party to 'make everything work out.' **You** *have to make it happen.* **You** *have to claw out your place in the world.* **You** *have to be the one to make your own success, to make your own way. You're going to get so busy and so bent over digging out a life for yourself you're going to forget Me and wander far from Me. To fix that, you're going to need Me."*

Our sin had not and would never diminish Yahweh's love for us, nor did it invoke any sort of curse on man or womankind. My supreme stupidity did not curse women for all time, despite what you may have heard. Cursed is permanent. Cursed is unredeemable. What Yahweh curses is that way forever. Even as I stood before Him in my fallen state, His words began to heal and bless, not kill or curse.

His prophecy of redemption through the serpent's demise left the door wide open for us to continue to walk in His favor if not in His presence. For me (hopefully for you) His promise to use woman in that plan removed forever any doubt that I have value, significance, and above all, that I am loved eternally and unconditionally.

MY GREATEST-GRANDSON

Yahweh's words described how Adam and I would now live and experience a world into which sin had entered. There would be no more Garden of Eden where every need was met before it existed. Things were going to be very different, and we needed to know what to expect. Preparing us for what was ahead was an act of love and mercy completely in keeping with His goodness.

Next He sacrificed some of His beloved animals so He could more appropriately dress us for life outside the Garden. He set us out of the Garden not to punish us but to protect us from eating of the Tree of Life, forever trapping us and our progeny in our unredeemed state. His plan of redemption had to be set in motion outside the Garden, and we were central to that plan.

Your Redeemer, Jesus, has a genealogy that traces all the way back to Adam. It's in your New Testament in the book called Luke. If it goes back to Adam, it goes back to Eve. Yes, I am the greatest-grandmother of Jesus, just as my Elohim promised when He revealed the plan of salvation in the Garden. The serpent may have tripped me, but my Greatest Grandson crushed his earless head.

THE SERPENT'S ONLY WEAPON

I learned something from my greatest stupidity I hope will help you recognize the serpent when he comes slinking around your world. He only has one tactic: Deceit. And though it's the only weapon in his arsenal, he's an expert at wielding it. He is deceit personified and will always tempt you with the same lie he did me. Here it is. Be on the lookout for it: "The Creator is holding something back from you."

Think about it. Every sin the serpent tempts you to is, "If you do this, you'll know more, get more, have more. You will *be more*. You won't need Elohim. You can be the lord of your life." It's so easy to fall for the empty promise of "more." The truth is Yahweh is all; when you have Him, there is nothing "more." Lord of your life? That's the biggest deception. Sin doesn't make you a lord. It makes you a slave.

The lie of "more" is the serpent's go-to because it's what happened to him that caused him to be cursed long before he slithered up to me in the Garden. The serpent's name is Satan, but before he was Satan, he was the angel Lucifer and actually had an exalted place on Elohim's holy mountain. I met him in his cold, scaly, legless, slithering snakehood, but from all accounts he wasn't always so hideous. At one time, he was covered from head to toe in sparking jewels and precious metals.

There was something wrong inside Lucifer. Maybe it was all the flashy clothes and exaltation; something gave him an inflated opinion of himself. He started reading his own press clippings and decided he could be like Elohim, even take His place. Of course, Elohim said, "Oh, no, you can't. There is none like me, and I will not share my glory with anyone," cursed him, and cast him off the holy mountain, where I suppose he waited indefinitely, until one day I came within earshot of "The Tree."

I know you've fallen for the serpent's lie in the past. Of course you have. It's part of being human. Everyone sins. I don't know what your supreme stupidity has been, but you've never been responsible for the fall of mankind. That's mine and mine alone. You need to know it's not what you've done, but what you do next that matters. You're probably wondering how you bounce back from a mistake so huge that your nametag reads "Responsible For The Fall of Mankind." I'm glad you asked.

YOU CAN'T UN-EAT THE FRUIT

What I suffered firsthand when I ate the fruit was the severing of relationship with my Elohim, with Yahweh, the one you call Father. You have a song you sing, "I once was lost but now I'm found, was blind but now I see." What I experienced when I disobeyed was the reverse of that. I experienced what you call "salvation" in the reverse, and I had no One to save me from what I'd done. I had hope of a coming Redeemer, but I had no Savior. I was now genuinely lost and blind.

There we were standing outside the Garden entrance, complete strangers to this part of creation. The world was enormous and unfamiliar. Elohim had told us what to expect, He'd made us covering to protect our bodies, and He'd given us a promise that someday He would send One to undo all I had done. But this was today and we were alone. Alone in a way we'd never been before: separated from the Creator.

We looked at each other, I hoping Adam had the answer, he hoping I did. For a long time all we did was gaze around, more than a little intimidated by the magnitude of the uncertainty before us. Okay, so "intimidated" is my euphemism for "afraid." Okay, so "afraid" is my euphemism for "terrified." And to be brutally honest, we weren't "more than a little" terrified. We were exponentially terrified.

Until I stood outside the Garden, I had never known fear for my life or fear of the unknown. I had never known fear of abandonment or failure. I had never known insecurity or loneliness or purposelessness. Until I ate the fruit I had never known loss or sadness. I had never known life-sucking regret. All of these things you may have lived with in your lifetime, I never knew. I was getting a crash course in fear, loss, and regret as a prerequisite to an honors degree in despair.

We had honestly nothing but the skins on our backs. We had no food. We had no shelter. Worst of all we had no direction and no definable purpose. The world lay wide open before us, but we had no understanding of what we were to do in or with it.

LEGS OF STONE

If you've ever suffered a monumental loss, you know surveying the landscape of life afterward can be dismal, to put it mildly. The terrain is fraught with purposelessness and desolation. It's not really the panoramic view that sends your mind into a dark downward spiral. You're not looking forward to any distant great horizons. You're struggling with the herculean task of discerning and taking the first small step toward simple survival. That's where Adam and I now stood, on the very precipice of despair.

At that moment, surrendering to the despair that beckoned from the darkness of my heart seemed a viable option. Why not just lie down and wait for death? If I had chosen despair, if this was the end of my story—Adam and I looking out at the distant mountains, separated forever from the Creator, facing a lifetime of miserable toil, inner torment, and suffocating regret—then that's a really gloomy story, and I promised you when we started, my story is not gloomy.

I didn't despair. I remembered.

Yahweh had given us two parameters for life in paradise. I blew one when I believed the lie of the serpent and did the one thing Yahweh told me not to. No matter how hard I tried or how sorry I was, I could never un-eat the fruit. You know what I'm talking about. You're offered a bite. You take it. As soon as you do, you realize it was a mistake, but you can't un-eat it. You can't give it back. There's no do-over. It's done.

The first thing you do is try to cover your sin (remember the fig leaves?). When that doesn't work, you defend yourself (the serpent deceived me), justify your sin (I thought Elohim would want me to be wiser), or blame someone else (thanks, Adam). It's not until you accept what you've done that you can be free from it, because you can't lay down what you don't hold in your hands.

THE GOODNESS OF ELOHIM

Staring blankly into the void of uncertainty before me, despair asked me to take its cold hand and walk off into a gray and lifeless sunset. As I contemplated whether to extend my hand and accept the invitation, I remembered. I remembered the **goodness** of my Elohim!

The crushing fear and utter hopelessness I'd felt subsided as I recalled His infinite goodness. He created paradise for the sole purpose of allowing Adam and I to enjoy it. He provided food before we were hungry, water before we were thirsty. He protected us; we'd never known fear. We'd never known pain. We were never cold, never hot. We had no understanding of "need" because every need was met before it existed. We never had to ask for any good thing because He automatically provided it.

Even when we disobeyed and forfeited forever our relationship with Him, it was His goodness that offered us the chance to heal, that covered our vulnerable flesh, that told us what to expect in our new lives, and that gave us the supreme hope of being the vehicle through which He would send the One who would redeem all we'd lost.

Yahweh's essence is goodness, and that can never change. I had changed, my environment had changed, but He didn't. He can't. The same goodness that created me and cared for me and communed with me was still *with* me. I couldn't see Him with my eyes anymore, but I vividly remembered His goodness and I knew it was and would always be part of His creation, even this strange and frightening part.

When I closed my eyes, I heard His voice, I remembered the sound of Him moving through the Garden, and (here's the best part) I remembered the peace that came with Him and my anticipation of His presence. Remembering filled me with something else new: hope. It was the memory of His great goodness that gave me hope and restrained my hand from the death grip of despair.

ON THE REBOUND

I think your question was how do you bounce back when you've messed up so monumentally that all creation now suffers because of your sin? You believe in the goodness of Yahweh and you choose to obey. I don't care what you've done or what's been done to you, there is nothing so awful that it can keep you from obeying your Elohim.

My circumstances and environment changed, my relationship with Elohim changed, but one thing did not: who He created me to be. The first command of

Eden remained, "Be fruitful! Multiply! Fill the earth and subdue it! And last but not least, reign!" Adam and I were still called, anointed, and appointed to reign. We were still in the plan. More than that, we were still the plan. Yahweh's directives weren't contingent on our success. He is the Eternally Unchangeable One. His plans would not be thwarted, even by our famous failure.

I don't care what sort of world you're facing, Yahweh is still good. Latch onto Him and never let go. That's how you keep writing your story until it comes to a non-gloomy conclusion. Believe me, had I not believed in His goodness, my story would have ended with my life being sucked into the noir vacuum of regret.

Your book of hymns—it's called Psalms in your Bible—has a song (or psalm, if you prefer) that succinctly sums up the answer to your question about rebounding:

I would have despaired, unless I had believed I would see the goodness of Yahweh in the land of the living (Psalm 27:13 NASB).

That word "believe" doesn't mean just give it a nod, "Oh, yes, I believe that's correct." It's the kind of belief that grabs hold of something and refuses to let go. That's the kind of belief it takes to keep going.

"Goodness" isn't your everyday, run-of-the-mill

goodness, either. That's a Hebrew superlative word. The closest I can translate it for you would be the "goodestness" of Yahweh. The "land of the living" is self-explanatory. It's here. This is the place you lick the bowl. This is the place you flourish. This is the place you choose to cling to Him.

I wasn't hoping to experience Yahweh's goodestness somewhere out in the future in another life. I fully expected (and was never disappointed) to see His goodestness every day, everywhere, all the time. So much was gone, but the breadcrumbs of His goodestness were right in front of me; I followed. I believed in the goodness of Yahweh and kept moving forward!

THIS TIME, IN OBEDIENCE

In His goodness and mercy, Yahweh had given us a second chance by way of His first assignment: "Flourish! Multiply!" I could never un-eat the fruit and go back, but nothing—not fear or loss or regret or a lying snake—would prevent me from pressing forward to obey the Creator I loved so dearly. The relationship had changed and I would never see Him again, but that could not keep me from flourishing. I chose to lick the bowl clean again!

I don't know what fruit you've eaten, but I know you'd love to un-eat it. You can't. You can never undo what's done and you can't hide it from Yahweh. Don't waste time devising ways to hide, justify, or blame your sin on someone or something. Those fig leaves with which Adam and I covered ourselves were useless, not to mention really unflattering.

There are moments in every life when you're faced with the horrible consequences of something you've done. Fixating on your sin and its consequences is paralyzing. It can seem impossible to move on. Believe me, I had legs and feet of stone when I stood outside the Garden's entrance for the first time.

If you're searching for the way forward, follow my footsteps; believe in the goodness of Yahweh. Keep moving, this time in obedience. You may have eaten the fruit today, maybe an hour ago, but you never have to eat it again and every breath you take is an opportunity to choose to flourish. I did it! You can! To tell the truth, it's not optional. The first words Elohim spoke to me are the same words He continues to speak to you: "Flourish! Multiply! Have a great time! I made this all for you!"

Adam and I didn't walk out of Eden and disappear into the mist. We didn't walk out and in our shame go opposite directions. We walked together, determined to obey Yahweh's first assignment.

The farther you walk with Yahweh, the more of His goodness you discover. I thought I'd experienced the full measure of His goodness and mercy when I left the Garden and was able to flourish in my new home. I had no idea how much of it He had still in store for me or how much I'd need it in our years ahead, as you'll see from the rest of my story.

MERCY, MERCY

You may know the story of Cain and Abel from Genesis 4 in your Bible. You may have heard it since your days in Sunday school class and heard it told in much the same manner as mine, a warning of things **not** to do. What's often glossed over in the telling of their story is the fact that they were my sons, my children, my precious ones, so their story is my story, too.

I don't talk much about Cain and Abel because there's no way to talk about it without being sad. It's a sad story. There's no way it can't be. For a parent, losing a child in any way is the quintessential sad story. Losing two children simultaneously because of the sin of one of them—well, that's why I don't talk about it much.

Before you start armchair analyzing, I am not in denial. I fully understand that my son Cain killed my son Abel. I know afterward Cain left and I never saw him again. I know these things deep down in my Knower where sacred things are stored. Believe me, I get it.

I am that mother of other mothers' nightmares, but hear

me when I say just as my eating the fruit in the Garden wasn't my legacy, neither is being the mother of loss. Yes, in the Garden I lost my relationship with Elohim through my sin. Outside the garden, my relationship with my two sons was stolen from me by Cain's sin. Still, I am not defined by the loss in my life; neither should you be.

MY HEART SONG

Adam and I moved forward and began to flourish, exactly as Elohim instructed. Having tended and looked after the Garden, we had a fundamental understanding of how to work and till the ground of our new world. It wasn't easy, but believing in Yahweh's goodness and remembering His command to me was ever-present.

There was a Deep Empty in the cool of the evening as I listened for His footsteps and held my breath to hear His voice. I knew He was there, just beyond my fingertips, at the end of my thoughts. So deep had been my walk with Him, I knew Him even in His absence. I held onto that "knowing" and the sweet memories of His presence as I moved into my new normal.

My heart song every day was "Flourish, Eve, flourish!" I sang it as I tilled the ground. I sang it as I gathered and prepared food. I sang it as I made new skins for Adam and me to wear. I didn't waste much time reminiscing about life in the Garden or regretting all I'd lost. I was too busy obeying and flourishing.

Sure, I remembered. I needed to remember. In fact, it was remembering that helped me press on in obedience. It was remembering that gave me hope.

EFFORTLESS FLOURISHING

There are two ways to live after a forbidden fruit binge. You can either become a slave to the serpent, which means spending your life working to undo or outperform your sin, or you can spend your life obeying Yahweh, which means a life of flourishing. Those are your choices: Serve the serpent or serve Yahweh. I chose to serve Yahweh.

I don't mean serving as in working to gain His love or approval. I wasn't pursuing obedience as a way to undo my sin. I wasn't trying to make amends. I wasn't doing the Get-A-Hug-From-Yahweh Jig. You know what I'm talking about. It's that dance you do in your day-to-day life to earn Yahweh's love. It's living as "If I can sing better, He'll love me; if I can serve more, He'll love me; if I can have a cleaner house or happier children, He'll love me; if I can keep my job, He'll love me."

I never had to earn His love. Neither do you. He loved me as much when I walked out of the Garden as He did when He took me from Adam's side. His love for me had not and would never change. Since He loved me after I caused the utter devastation of His creation, you can be sure nothing you have done or can do will change His love for you. I don't know what you've done, Precious, but your sin is not greater than His love.

Let that truth become the foundation of your life. Yahweh loves you. Unconditionally. Eternally. Unreservedly. When you know that, I mean really know that, flourishing happens effortlessly. Being loved like that by the all-powerful Creator of the universe is the ultimate freedom.

I wasn't obeying to appease Him or earn something back from Him. Remember, I didn't have your Ten Commandments. I didn't have a religious system of do's and don'ts, of ways to dress, speak and eat, of verses to memorize, and a quota of lost souls to evangelize. All I had was His command to flourish and multiply, fill and subdue, and reign.

TWO-LEGGED SNAKES

When you break it all down, that's the same command He gives you, although thousands of years of rules, laws, and traditions have made it more complicated. Granted, after sin entered the world via yours truly, Yahweh implemented safeguards to keep you from harm because outside the Garden the world was a much more dangerous place. His "laws" (if you want to call them that) were never meant to keep you from any good thing. The opposite, their whole purpose is to help you flourish safely in a fallen world.

I hope you recognize the scheme of the serpent in twisting Yahweh's protection into something oppressive and limiting. Yahweh doesn't want you limited. Yahweh wants you flourishing. Anytime there's even a whisper that Yahweh's safeguards are to keep you from living life-life, you can bet there's a snake in the bushes somewhere. Not all snakes slide around on their stomachs. Most stand on two feet, but you can learn to recognize the sound of a snake's voice.

In the Garden, Yahweh told the serpent that I and all my daughters would be mortal enemies of him and his kind. You have to know when the Creator of the universe told the serpent "And I will put enmity between you and the woman," He wasn't just saying women don't like legless reptiles. He was saying, "Because you have deceived her, she now knows your voice, and she'll recognize your presence even when others don't.

"She'll walk into a room and sense you're there. She will hate you when she smells you in her house, in her school, in her workplace, in the grocery store. She will sense you, she will see you, and she will recognize your voice and expose you."

LIVE BOLDLY!

The serpent wants to limit you because he knows you are powerful. He recognizes you as *ezer k'enegdo*. He wants to trip you with one of his lies so you'll fall into his quicksand of shame, fear, and regret. He'd *really* like for you to meet his friend Despair.

So he whispers to you "Did Elohim really say you couldn't do that?" The answer is yes. In order to protect you, Elohim has put a fence around certain trees in this world. But when He told me not to eat the fruit of one particular tree, He was telling me I **could** eat from **every other** tree. If I hand you a box of one million pieces of chocolate and tell you not to eat the one in the corner, are you really going to pine for that one little nougat-filled candy or are you going to devour the other 999,999 truffles?

Leaving batter in the bowl doesn't make Yahweh love you more or undo anything you've done. Stop holding back. Stop limiting yourself by living small because of something you've done. Stop being afraid you don't measure up. Stop trying to un-eat the fruit. Stop worrying you'll be exposed. News flash: You're already exposed to Yahweh. You don't need to run hide in the bushes.

Yahweh loves you, and He's already prepared a covering for you much greater than the skins He made for me. Your covering is the righteousness of the One who crushed the head of the serpent. Whatever you've done, it's covered. You can live boldly knowing when Yahweh looks at you, He sees your Covering.

WHAT MOTHER COULD WANT MORE!

So Adam and I flourished, and before long, the multiplying part of our lives started. I could feel creation happening inside me. Adam and I and Yahweh were moving forward into something new.

Our first son, Cain, was born and I rejoiced. Yahweh had given me a son, a brand-new life, the first born not from the ground but from my body. One more reminder of the supreme goodness of my Elohim!

When I had a second son, I named him Abel and reveled again in Yahweh's blessings. It hadn't been easy, this wasn't paradise, but Yahweh's goodness had sustained us. Now we were a family. Life was good and every morning I rose determined to flourish more than the day before.

As our boys grew, I filled their minds and hearts with stories of our time in the Garden, of how their dad and I walked and talked with Yahweh. I knew they could never know Him as intimately as I had, but I was determined they'd know of His goodness.

I told them how Yahweh's goodness extended beyond the confines of the Garden and transcended the depths of my sin. I taught them to look for His goodness in His creation. We'd spend time every day talking about where we'd seen Elohim's majesty or sovereignty.

My boys were quick to learn. They would tell me of a breathtaking sunrise or a towering tree laden with fruit. Cain would talk of the bounty of his crops; Abel of the multiplication of his flocks. They were seeing Yahweh's goodness firsthand. What mother could ask for more!

We'd taught them to return part of their blessings to Elohim, not because there was a law or they needed to appease Him or earn something from Him, but simply because He is good. They learned, and one day each brought an offering: Abel the first and best of his flock; Cain—well, Cain brought something as well but not his best or most prized.

CAIN'S HEART

Yahweh knew Cain's heart was not in his offering. He knew Cain was holding back his trust, and He knew how dangerous that was. So did I. Yahweh wanted Cain's heart because He knew the serpent was lurking about the fields waiting for the moment to strike at my boys' heels; waiting for the chance to deceive them, the way he had me.

Cain's heart was not with Yahweh because he didn't know Him. He knew of Him from his dad and me, but He'd never spent time with Him as we had. Knowing about Yahweh is not the same as knowing Him.

I didn't have a Bible so I could read "about" Him. I had

His face, His voice, His presence, and my experience with Him in the cool of the evening before I ate that fruit. I had real experience to pass to my sons, and I did, through stories about Him and through my daily choice to serve Him. They had all I could give them, but the choice to trust in the Creator of my stories, the One I loved and lived was theirs. They would have to choose to believe.

Cain had heard the stories, he believed Yahweh was real, he believed Yahweh was good, but he did not know Him. I don't care if you can recite your entire Bible from cover to cover, if you only know *about* Yahweh, you can be Cain all over again. Yahweh doesn't want your servitude; He wants your heart. He wants you to know Him and His goodness firsthand, because when you do, you will love Him.

Yahweh didn't hide His displeasure with Cain's offering, and Cain became angry. Yahweh sought Cain out, and spoke to him, just as He'd done with Adam and me. "Cain, what's going on? Why are you so mad? Why do you look so down? Talk to me. Something's wrong. Tell me about it."

Do you think that Elohim did not know what was going on with Cain? Of course He did, just as He knew where Adam and I were and what we'd done that day in the Garden. He asks rhetorical questions to give us the opportunity to know the answer, not because He doesn't know. Yahweh came down to speak to Cain so Cain could confess what was in his heart and be healed.

YOUR GREATEST CHEERLEADER

When He questioned Cain it was to save him from making the same mistake his father and I made. Cain didn't respond, so Yahweh spoke the truth to him: "If you do what is right, will you not be accepted? But if you do not do what is right, sin is crouching at your door; it desires to have you, but you must rule over it" (Gen. 4:7).

You've probably never thought of Elohim as your greatest cheerleader. If not, you don't know Him the way I do, the way He wanted Cain to know Him. He was saying, "Just do the right thing, Cain. If you don't, sin is waiting for you, just as it was waiting for your mom and dad. It wants to rule you, but you have to master it. You've got this! You can do it!"

You may be just on this side of the door from a sin that's knocking. I don't know what it is, and I'm not being prophetic. I just know, because I've lived in this fallen world just as you have, that in any given 30 seconds of most of our lives, sin is just on the other side of the door, a mere knob-turn away.

That's the nature of life in this fallen world. But you

don't face that door all by yourself. Yahweh is your cheerleader! His voice is there to stop you as you grasp the knob: "What's on the other side of that door is going to eat you up. It won't make your life better. What's on the other side of that door wants to kill you. You're going to have to master it. And you can! You've got this! I'm here to help!"

Cain turned the knob and walked through the door and out of my life forever. He was banished from Yahweh's presence when he killed his brother and left his body in a field. In one instant I went from being the mother of two sons growing to know and love the goodness of my Elohim to the mother of a murdered son and also the mother of his murderer.

Give me a second.

Thanks.

Reliving that moment always leaves me a little bit breathless.

Learning of the death of Abel and exile of Cain, I felt a familiar, cold despair wrap around my heart. I was no stranger to this depth of hopelessness. I'd known it in the Garden, cowering under leaves with bitten fruit in my hand—the sudden emptiness, the desperate regret, the deafening tension. That first time, it was something

I'd done; me, all by myself. I'd sinned. This time, the grief that threatened to destroy me from the inside out was done to me. And nightmare of nightmares, it was my son—my firstborn child, gift from Elohim, the new beginning, the first manifestation of our thriving and moving on—who had committed this unbelievable atrocity. And he'd done it to *my son*.

Elohim gave me Cain. He gave me Abel. They were my tangible reminders of His goodness and mercy, and now they were gone. Forever. Yet, I turned to Yahweh. I clutched hope to my aching heart and prepared to keep living.

I know it's taken us a few pages to get here, but the best part, the most important part of my story is just getting started. So let's move on, because that's exactly what I did.

MOVING ON

Years earlier when I ate from the Tree of the Knowledge of Good and Evil, do you know what I found? I found there were many things I'd be a whole lot better off not knowing. You know what I'm talking about. Aren't there things about the depth of the depravity of humans and about our sin nature you just wish you could un-know? If only we could.

We can't. What we can do is learn to walk through a world where both good and evil are ever-present and not have our legs turn to stone. That can happen. Evil can paralyze you with fear, with anger, with grief. I'm saying this as one who has experienced firsthand the power of both good and evil. Yahweh's good is my life's breath. The world's evil can leave you breathless. It almost did me.

It's one thing when you mess up; when you have a moment of weakness and stupidity, momentarily believe a lie, and cause the fall of mankind. It's completely different when evil barges in and robs you of Yahweh's precious gifts and it's not your fault. I lost both my sons and my world came crashing down, but this time, I didn't do it.

Yes, I ate the fruit. Yes, I caused the fall. Yes, I brought sin into the world. Yes, I lost my relationship with Elohim. I did all that. I owned it, and then I left it behind and obeyed. I flourished. I multiplied. I taught my sons to flourish and multiply. I taught them of Yahweh's goodness. I taught them to give back to Him because He'd given everything. I had eaten the forbidden fruit, but I hadn't let sin define me or stop me from obeying. I was doing everything "right."

Still, Cain killed Abel.

BAD THINGS HAPPEN

Skipping through the garden of life smelling the flowers, feeling the sun on your back, and enjoying His blessings, it's easy to sing praise songs to Yahweh. A tornado rips a half-mile-wide path right through the middle of your garden, destroying all your beautiful flowers, leaving nothing but a mound of dirt and dead shrubbery, the music stops mid-note and you become a functional mute. Believe me, I know how hard it is to look at a pile of dirt, sticks, and stones and praise Yahweh's goodness. Staring at the lifeless body of Abel in that blood-soak field, there was no song in my mouth either.

Once sin came storming into the world because of what I did, it set in motion the possibility—okay, okay, the inevitability that bad things happen even when you're doing everything, "right"; even when you believe in the goodness of and obey Yahweh. The tendency sometimes is to blame or become angry at Yahweh when bad things happen. Believe me, I get that, but Yahweh never causes or condones evil. His essence is Goodness and that by definition precludes His association with Badness.

Yahweh did not cause Cain to kill Abel. In fact, because He is so good, He tried to stop him. He tried to warn Cain against the evil that was luring him to that sinful act. Yahweh stepped back into the story to have a real-time conversation with Cain, personally and intimately.

The story is recorded in Genesis 4 of your Bible. As you read it, you hear Yahweh coaching Cain in the skill of sin management. Yahweh inspired its inclusion in your Bible so you will know deeply and surely that He is *for* you, just as He was for Cain. He always tries to save us from our own stupidity. Always.

If you think my world was shaken when I left the Garden, well, you're right, but at least I knew that was my fault. I lost everything **by what I did**. Not this. This time it wasn't my fault. This time when a whirlwind tore through my garden, I didn't do it and there was nothing, I mean *nothing* that could undo it. Again.

OUT OF ORDER

I never blamed Yahweh for what happened to my sons, but that doesn't mean I didn't suffer when I lost them or didn't mourn for them. I was devastated when Cain killed Abel. I can't pretend I wasn't. I can't pretend I just stood up from that blood-soaked ground, dusted my hands, and said, "Yahweh, I know you're good and that you cause all things to work out for good to those who love you and are called according to your purpose," turned and skipped away.

If that's how you visualize me reacting to that horror, try again. I didn't stand; I fell. I didn't wipe the dust from my hands; I beat the ground with them. I didn't tell Yahweh He was good; I screamed in anguish. I won't ask you to try to imagine you were in my place, because that's too cruel. If you're a parent, this is one scenario you never want to even imagine. But I promised you the whole story, and this is part of the story, though I'm sure you can see now why I don't talk about it much.

I mourned the loss of Abel. I mourned the loss of Cain. I can't tell you which was worse, Abel's death or Cain's exile. It doesn't matter. I suffered that loss that is unspeakable because it's unnatural; it's out of order. It's the loss that makes others want to turn away, to not look because it's truly unbearable. Without Yahweh's goodness and mercy, I could not have borne it. Neither can you. His mercy saved me from loss so profound it almost took my last breath; it will save you, too.

I finally stood. I took a step. I breathed. There was no support group of bereaved parents to run to. I couldn't pull out my Bible and read the comforting words of the psalmists. I couldn't call my best friend, my sister, or my mother. I had none of those. I had Adam, he had me, and we knew Yahweh was good, even as we buried Abel and watched helplessly as Cain walked out of our lives forever.

Standing beside a mound of freshly turned earth, Cain's silhouette a distant speck on the horizon, I thought of Yahweh watching Adam and me turn our backs and walk out of the Garden. Did His heart ache like mine? Did He have to refrain from running after us as we walked away from the paradise He'd created just for us? Was He breathless even as He was being holy?

Then I remembered His words as He lovingly counseled us about our future, and suddenly, sadly recognized the emotion I'd heard in His voice that day. For the first time I understood, as much as humanly possible, the depth of His loss, and it made me love Him more.

THE SONG YAHWEH LOVES

Your Bible is jam-packed with songs about Yahweh's goodness. I love them all and I'm sure you have your favorites, but there's one in particular Yahweh loves.

He taught it to the army of Israel just before they went into battle. When they obeyed Him and sang Yahweh's favorite song, they didn't have to fight; their enemies dropped dead before they could unsheathe their swords. It goes like this: "Yahweh is good, and His goodness endures forever." Those are the only words, sung to various tunes, but He loves it.

You probably have had songs you just can't get enough of; this is Yahweh's. He loves to hear us sing it and tells us to over and over. Knowing what I know about Yahweh, He doesn't tell us to sing about His unending goodness because He needs to hear it. Believe me, He knows His own goodness. He tells us to sing it because He knows we need to remember His goodness, especially when our world is shaken to its very foundation.

PRESSING ON

I will never say it was easy to keep pressing on in obedience after that, but I knew my Elohim had told me to flourish, and I knew that didn't mean only as long as the sun is shining and the flowers in my garden are blooming. Through the loss I experienced when I left the Garden and when I lost my sons, I realized there is a natural cycle of change Yahweh has programmed into our human existence. Recognizing the stages of this natural cycle helped me walk through them. It can help you, too.

The four stages of change are what I call The Status Quo, The Shaking, The Sadness, and The New Normal. You need to understand these stages because the third stage can be a little tricky to navigate. It's actually possible to get stuck in the labyrinth of sadness and not be able to find your way out.

The first stage, The Status Quo, is where we like to be. It's when you're just simply living your day-to-day life. You live in a certain place, you get up every day at a certain time, you eat certain food, wear certain clothing, go do certain things, come back to your certain place, rest your head on your certain pillow, then get up the next day and do it all again. Life is predictable. Life is smooth. Life is certain.

If you've lived very long, you know there is going to be a shaking in your life on a pretty regular basis. If you don't find yourself currently in the middle of this cycle, you've probably either just come out of it cycle or you're about to go into it. The Shaking stage is where some agent of change steps into your certain, predictable, smooth world and shakes things up. It could be a loss. It could be an addition. Maybe your job changes, your family changes, your status changes, your address changes, your tax rate changes. Sometimes this agent of change is something you do, and sometimes the agent of change is done to you. Having been both the Doer and the Done-To, I can tell you firsthand, that part doesn't matter. Something changes and the resultant next step in the same.

Tricky step three is The Sadness. When Adam and I left the Garden, we walked smack-dab into immeasurable sadness because of the cataclysmic shaking we'd suffered. Believing in Yahweh's goodness kept us moving through that sadness. When Cain and Abel were born, Adam and I went through a less devastating period of sadness, because even an addition is a change and change causes an adjustment to be made and adjustments, even good ones, bring a natural sadness.

The fourth step is The New Normal. You've experienced change, walked through sadness, things are different than they were, but it's your new normal and soon becomes your status quo. When I left the Garden, my world was shaken. I experienced sadness so profound it threatened to destroy me…but it didn't. I moved through that sadness and found my new normal: Life with Adam and our boys, obeying and flourishing in our new status quo. And then my world was shaken again.

I don't know where you are in this cycle. You may be happily exploring your new normal on the way to settling into status quo. You may have just experienced a shaking and have started into the cycle of sadness. If you're in any of those stages and you're still moving, good. Keep going! Moving is imperative. Sometimes, however, you get stuck in The Sadness. When that happens it can seem there's no way out. There is. I made it through. Let me show you the way.

GETTING OFF THE GRIEF-GO-ROUND

What makes the third stage of change so tricky is that sadness (a/k/a mourning) and grief look so much alike. They wear their hair the same, they shop at the same boutique and wear almost the same size clothes. They even have a lot of the same mannerisms. Here's the all-important difference. Mourning is like a story. It has a beginning, middle, and an end. Grieving starts and never stops. Somewhere in the midst of sadness you get lost in the story, and you forget how to make it stop. You forget there's an end and you lose sight of the off switch. You are trapped on a grief-go-round.

It's easy to get lost in grief. Maybe it's because you think you're honoring someone or making a memorial to something. Maybe you think your grief is proof of your love or devotion to someone or something. In your sadness, you may say things such as, "I'll never be the same again. I'll never love like that again. I'll never do that again." Without knowing, you make a vow.

Making that vow is like hitting the "Start" switch on the

grief-go-round. It starts going around and around and around and you can't reach the "Stop" button. Don't be afraid. Don't lose hope. There's Someone whose arms are long and strong enough to flip the "Stop" switch for you.

A NEW WARDROBE

The words of the Prophet Isaiah recorded in your Bible declare when your Redeemer comes, He will "appoint to the mourners of Zion, and to give them a crown for ashes, the oil of joy for mourning, a garment of praise for the spirit of grief."[5] Your Redeemer arrived around two thousand years ago. His name is Jesus, He accomplished all He came to do, and as prophesied in these words, part of His assignment was stopping the grief-go-round.

The mourners of Zion about which Isaiah wrote are those who've had their status quo shaken and are walking through the stage of sadness. In Isaiah's time, it was the practice for someone in mourning or other severe emotional distress to cover their heads (sometimes their entire bodies) with ashes. Ashes represent emptiness and purposelessness. They're the worthless remnant of something that at one time had meaning.

When you burn a piece of wood it serves its function of keeping you warm or cooking your food, but when the wood is burned up, all that's left is a useless pile of ashes. A crown, on the other hand represents consecration, purpose, life, honor, and accomplishment. In the midst of mourning, on your way to your new normal, Jesus' promise is for new life, new purpose, and new accomplishments.

As if ashes in their hair weren't bad enough, mourners used to pair the ashes with garments made from sackcloth. Sackcloth is woven from goat hair, or sometimes hemp if goat hair happened to be in short supply. Both materials are dark, smelly, and extremely coarse, itchy, and uncomfortable. Picture a burlap jumpsuit. On your worst day, you looked and smelled infinitely better than mourners of Isaiah's time.

The garment of praise referred to by Isaiah was a brightly colored jacket so different in its color and its makeup you could not possibly confuse it with sackcloth. It's your blingy jacket; the one with the sequin appliqués in just the right color to bring out your eyes. That's the one Jesus wants to drape across your shoulders.

Oil, in what you consider "ancient" times, had many uses. It could be used for sanctifying or for setting something in place. Kings were anointed into their positions of permanent authority by the application of oil. Jesus gives you the oil of joy to **replace** mourning, not set it in place, because the other use for oils, in Isaiah's time and yours, is as a healing agent. Many oils are used therapeutically because of their soothing and healing abilities. Jesus anoints you with the oil of joy to heal your heart.

Most healing oils are very aromatic. Can you imagine what the oil of joy might smell like; if joy had a scent, what it would be? Maybe like the Garden before the serpent, where the air was filled with the fragrance of every flower and fruit imaginable. Remembering that smell definitely makes me joyful. Regardless, you know you'd want to dab some joy on your wrists and maybe a little behind each ear.

Putting ashes in your hair and walking around in smelly, dreary, uncomfortable clothes is the antithesis of flourishing. On the other hand, a diamond tiara, a flashy jacket, and some new perfume are exactly the wardrobe you need to flourish. You don't put on this jacket to "dress up" and cover up your hurt and pain, but to announce to everyone you've decided to live. You've decided to thrive.

Jesus wants to adorn you in these because you're going someplace new. You're not stopping to build a house in Sadness Valley. You're moving to New Normalville. When you get there, you're going to turn some heads and you are going to flourish.

INVITED IN

Seven hundred years after Isaiah wrote those words, Jesus stood on a mountain and opened His mouth to teach for the first time in His ministry. The very first words out of His mouth were "Blessed are the poor in spirit, for theirs is the Kingdom of heaven. Blessed are those who mourn, for they shall be comforted." It's in your Bible in the book of Matthew, Chapter 5, if you want to look it up.

For 400 of those 700 years (from Malachi to Matthew), Yahweh was silent. No prophets. No signs. No wonders. Nothing. Then one night in Bethlehem, a baby cries and Yahweh breaks His silence. Jesus didn't start His ministry until after He was baptized by John and tempted by the serpent. When it was time for Him to speak, the first significant words out of His mouth weren't to the rich, the powerful, the scholars, the religious leaders. He speaks directly and personally to those who are sad—and He gives them hope. My good Elohim always gives hope!

In times of mourning, hope lives in knowing your sadness will end. It's designed to come to an end, not be the end, and it ends when you're comforted. The word "comfort" Jesus spoke to "those who mourn" has two parts. The first part means "invited in." Jesus isn't just going to give you a tissue, pat your hand, and smile sympathetically. When you're really sad, when your status quo has been shaken and you are mourning, Jesus gets it. He opens His arms and invites you into His embrace.

Because He's eternal, the spirit in Him was there when Adam and I left the Garden, trembling and broken. He was there the next time our world got set on edge when Cain killed Abel. Just so, He was there when your world tilted on its axis. He knows what you're going through. Wherever you are in the cycle Jesus says quite honestly to you, "I get it, but you're blessed when you mourn because I'll invite you in."

The second half of the word "comfort" is so powerful. It means "to breathe." It's not just the staying-alive kind of breathing. It's when you can finally let go the white-knuckled grip with which you've held your world together for what seems an eternity. It's the breath you take when you at long last find a pair of arms wide and strong enough to catch you, and you fall into them and melt into their bosom as every struggle-tensed muscle in your body relaxes. It's the deep, calming sigh that finally comes after you've beaten the ground until your fists bleed and you've screamed in anguish until your voice is gone.

When your world has been torn apart and you're so sad you think the shattered remnants of it may fall out from under you, Jesus opens His arms and invites you in so you can let go; so you can breathe. Jesus said, "When you mourn, come in to Me. I will help you breathe." His invitation for those who mourn is for there to be an end, to be comforted. The comfort He offers brings the grief-go-round to a grinding halt so you can finally get off.

ASHES ON YOUR TIARA

Just as Yahweh didn't design mourning to be permanent, He also didn't design it to be disregarded. Sometimes you want to leap-frog over sadness because you just don't think you can cry one more tear. You're done with mourning. You have had it with sadness. You've faced so much sadness in your life, you just refuse to be unhappy, no matter how badly your world gets shaken. Because you've been here before, the temptation is strong to just hop right over to new normal. After all, at the end of the day it's all going to work out because Yahweh's good, right?

Of course He is, and because He is, yes, He does work all things, even earth-shattering shakings, together for good, but this is not a question of Yahweh's goodness. It's a question of whether or not you'll allow mourning to serve its divine purpose of renewal and increased strength. That's its purpose, you know. That's why it has a beginning, a middle, and an end, and why it's so important you don't avoid it or run out in the middle of your story.

I know sometimes it seems sadness will destroy you so you just *will* it to end. You stick a rhinestone tiara on your ash-laden head, pull a brightly colored coat over your sackcloth, slap some dollar store toilet water on your wrists, and walk out on sadness like nothing's happened. Before long, you'll come home to find Yahweh waiting for you on the stoop. "What's going on? Why do you look so down? Talk to me. Something's wrong. Tell me about it." Familiar questions?

Yahweh knows what's wrong. Your ash covered rhinestones aren't His diamonds, there's sackcloth sticking out around the collar of your imitation praise garment, and Honey, you smell like a goat. You can't hide your heart from Yahweh. He wants you to realize even though you're all dressed up on the outside, your heart is not healed. Left untended, a sorrowful heart becomes a hard, calloused heart.

STUCK IN THE MIDDLE

Elohim designed women to embody the full spectrum of emotions because we're created in His image, in all of His fullness. That spectrum includes mourning and rejoicing. If you watch the pendulum of a grandfather clock, it swings equally from one side to the other. If you stop the pendulum's swing halfway through on one side, it stops halfway through on the other side as well because it's precisely balanced.

What you won't mourn you also can't rejoice. It's just like the clock's pendulum: You mourn less, you rejoice less, you mourn less, you rejoice less, until finally it just stops altogether. You're stuck in the middle, in a state of constant apathy. Sure, there's no sadness. There's also no joy.

Yahweh made you to feel. It isn't going to weaken you. It isn't going to break you into a million pieces. It *is* going to cause you to swing all the way back to the rejoicing side. The fullness of mourning produces the fullness of rejoicing.

CHANGING THE ENVIRONMENT

Psalm 84 talks about the journey that, sooner or later, we're all required to take through the valley of mourning. It's called the Valley of Baka [6]in your Bible, and that word Baka is from the Hebrew root *beku* or *bakah*, which means "weeping" or "to weep." Amazing things happen for those who travel through the valley of weeping.

"As they pass through the Valley of Baka, they make it a place of springs" (vs. 6). First and foremost, you need to grab hold of the words "they pass through." The momentum that shoved you into the valley of weeping is for you to use to get out. Springs don't bubble up when you *camp* in the valley. You can't allow yourself to be comfortable with the weeping. Don't survey the lot. Don't hang pictures. This is not where you stop. You are passing through.

Now shut your eyes and imagine yourself walking through a dry, desolate valley. See each foot as it sets down on the parched, cracked ground. Hold your foot in place and watch as water begins to seep out around its edges. When you raise your foot, a spring of cool, clean water gurgles happily where before was dust and death. Your mere presence, the very act of you making this painful journey transforms the desert of desolation into the habitat of happiness. You change the environment just by being there.

Verse 7 says those who pass through the valley of mourning "go from strength to strength, till each appears before Elohim in Zion." You are heading to a new normal where your assignment to flourish requires a different capacity for and a different magnitude of strength. Your world has changed. You have new things to do, new assignments to fulfill, new bowls to lick.

Your new normal will be spilling over with new ways to flourish, but you can't flourish in New Normalville with the same strength you had in your old status quo. New strength happens when you walk all the way through the Valley of Baka. You're moving from "strength to strength," from flourish to flourish, with the end game of being in the presence of Elohim.

The end is Elohim. Your glorious, majestic, sovereign Elohim! I told you when we started He's the beginning. He's also the end. You call Him the Alpha and the Omega, and so He is. You press in and press on, knowing His goodness will lead to an end of your sadness and you'll start again, this time from a position of new and renewed strength.

There's a party going on, just the other side of the Valley of Baka, complete with a disco ball, a live band, and a seemingly endless dessert buffet. You'll walk into that room wearing your tiara, your blingy jacket, new perfume, and heads will turn. I should warn you to add a comfortable (yet stylish) pair of shoes to your new wardrobe, because one thing I know from experience, when you reach the end of this journey, you will dance!

WHAT'S IN A NAMETAG?

After you've walked through your valley of weeping, you don't just get over it. You don't just make do. You're not just okay. Yahweh says that after mourning, you dance. "There is a time for everything, and a season for every activity under the heavens: a time to be born and a time to die, a time to plant and a time to uproot, a time to kill and a time to heal, a time to tear down and a time to build, a time to weep and a time to laugh, *a time to mourn and a time to dance.*"[7] Dancing follows mourning because Yahweh said "Flourish!" and He's never rescinded that command.

I love to dance but never learned how to really "kick up the dust," as Adam calls it, until after losing Abel and Cain. It's true. When Adam and I left the Garden, we didn't spend nearly as much time dancing as we have since walking through the Valley of Baka. Sure, we were flourishing, and I often did the Flourish Shuffle as I worked alongside Adam. Every now and then he'd even shuffle up next to me as we planted or harvested.

I bet you've never seen the Flourish Shuffle, right? It's a little right-left-right, left-right-left sideways shuffle with a bit of a cha-cha arm and hip twist thrown in. You should try it. The timing of it fits perfectly with my heart song, "Flourish, Eve, flourish!" and you can sing that song as you shuffle; just put your name in the middle. Try it sometime. It made my days working in the fields and caring for my sons pass more joyfully.

As much fun as the Flourish Shuffle is (I still do it, by the way) after the tragedy of losing Cain and Abel, after mourning them, after walking through the valley of weeping, I learned to dance before Yahweh in a whole new way. Dancing before Yahweh creates an atmosphere of praise and worship He loves. He doesn't love it because He needs to be reassured of His majesty and sovereignty and not because He particularly likes the dust storm I generate. He loves it because He knows it comes from a heart that's fully healed and a life that's vibrantly flourishing.

AND WE DANCED!

Mercifully, not everyone experiences the same degree of tragedy. I don't know what, who, or even if you've mourned in your lifetime. I do know at some point if you haven't, you will. When you come to your valley of weeping, walk all the way through, finish it. That's the important part. It's not about the degree of tragedy you experience. What leads to dancing is finishing the mourning; seeing it through to the end so you can wash the ashes out of your hair, get dressed in your praise garments, and dance with abandon before Yahweh.

Adam and I reached the other side of the Valley of Baka together, and we danced! Our hearts were healed, we were stronger than ever, and we were ready for a new life. Our assignment in Elohim's beautiful world had not changed because of anything we'd been through any more than it had changed by what I'd done: "Flourish! Multiply!" We did both and before long Yahweh gave us a third son. We named him Seth, and danced again!

LIFE HAPPENS

Before He made Adam and me, Elohim made an environment that was perfect for us to flourish. Then He created us to be just like Him. One wonderful characteristic of Himself He deposited in me, in you, in all women, is the ability to create an environment for life to flourish. Remember, we started as a rib, protecting and sustaining life. Then Elohim gave us a womb, the quintessence of a life-nurturing environment.

You know, of course, women do nothing to make the womb work. When I carried my sons, I did nothing to make my body produce and nurture those babies. I was just me. I ate. I slept. I cooked. I worked with Adam in the fields. I didn't cause my blood pressure to go up or down. I didn't cause blood flow to be greater or lesser to those babies. I didn't cause nourishment to be passed to them. I let my body do what Elohim designed it to do and life happened.

Please don't hear me say you were designed only to have babies or that if you don't have children you are any less powerful, less important, or less woman than the rest of the world's population with two X chromosomes. That's not at all what I'm talking about. What I am saying and what I really want you to understand is you were designed to create an environment for life to thrive—in the home, in the workplace, in the community, and in the Kingdom of Yahweh. You do that by being the woman Yahweh has called you to be, whether that entails having physical children or not.

Physical flourishing is not the only flourishing Yahweh calls us to, nor is it the only type of flourishing environment we create. Women generate atmospheres where spiritual life thrives as well. We are natural nurturers, physically and spiritually. Elohim gave women a womb because our bodies are the physical representation of what we do spiritually. Spiritually, when you walk in the fullness of all Elohim created you to be you, spiritual life happens.

MORE THAN ENOUGH

Many women don't know who they are or what they're supposed to do. One reason is because roles and expectations of women get distorted by the many voices in your world; so many voices pulling you in so many directions. Yahweh tells you to do one thing, the same thing He told me: flourish. In flourishing you automatically produce an environment for others to flourish. *That* is who you are. *That* is what you're supposed to do. Just as nothing you do and nothing that's done to you can stop you from obeying Yahweh, it also cannot change who you were created to be. You are *ezer k'enegdo,* you are *ishah,* and you are more than enough.

You are strong and strategic. You build up, you unify, and you shield. You are wise and discerning. As a woman, walking in the fullness of all you were created to be, those qualities naturally emanate from you. When you walk in the room, the environment transforms to one of strength and confidence. When you walk in the room, you bring an atmosphere of unity. When you walk in the room, you bring protection because you can discern the serpent's attacks and shield those less familiar with his voice. You're not charging in with a sword and shield or rushing the stage and grabbing the spotlight. As a woman intimately acquainted with your Creator and aware of the magnificent strength you were designed to embody, you simply show up.

MY TRUE NAMETAG

We all wear nametags; labels we've given ourselves or been tagged with. I don't know what yours says. I don't know if it's a nametag you've peeled the back off of and applied yourself, or if it's a yellow sticky note someone slapped on you. I do know if it doesn't have some version of "Strong, redeemed, chocolate-eyebrowed, loved and highly esteemed, wise *ezer k'enegdo*" written on it, you should rip it off.

You've seen my nametag, the one that says "Responsible For The Fall of Mankind." I wear that so those who aren't well acquainted with me will recognize me. I have another nametag those who know me well will understand. I hope you're one of those. My true nametag reads something very different.

Seth grew up in a bowl-licking, life-living, dust-cloud-generating environment because I learned to stare down the black-hole-beckon of regret and let hope rule. I learned believing in Yahweh's goodness is so much more powerful than the siren's call of despair. I learned to flourish and worship through life's most horrendous tragedies. I learned Elohim's perpetual goodness and love transcend all dimensions and all evil, regardless of where that evil originates. I learned who Yahweh created me to be: a woman who brings strength, unity, perspective and protection into every circumstance and environment.

My legacy begins not at the end of your Genesis Chapter 3, leaving the Garden in shame, fear, and regret. That was only the preface to my story. My legacy begins with the last line in your Genesis Chapter 4: "And as for Seth, to him also a son was born; and he named him Enosh. Then men began to call on the name of Yahweh."

During Seth's lifetime, those who'd never walked in the Garden with Yahweh, who'd never seen His glory or majesty began to call on His name and to seek Him. They began to hunger for a relationship with Him and look to Him as their Elohim. They began to believe, and it was because of Seth. It was because Seth was born. It was because I didn't get stuck on the grief-go-round or fall for the lie that because of the tragedy I'd experienced, I couldn't thrive—I *shouldn't* thrive. I'd fallen for a lie from an unfamiliar voice before, but not this time. This time I chose to listen to the voice of my Elohim deep within me, and I heard Him loud and clear: "Get chocolate in your eyebrows!"

Let me assure you, Seth was not the perfect son. He was good, of course, but he wasn't any more perfect than any other child. It wasn't Seth's perfection that led men to call on Yahweh. It was because Adam and I loved Yahweh, demonstrated that love through obedience and perseverance, and in so doing created an atmosphere of flourishing for our son and the next generations. It was because of our unfaltering belief in the goodness and love of Yahweh.

Every woman wants her legacy to be that because of her story, because of all she went through, because she created a flourishing, nurturing environment, because she *believed,* others called on the name of Yahweh. My rightful, eternal nametag, the one I joyfully wear, the one I hope you'll remember from now on when you hear my name, reads, "Eve. Because she believed, men began to call on the name of Yahweh."

Your story is still being written. Your legacy is yet to be determined. Make it one you'll happily write across your eternal nametag!

YAHWEH'S GREATEST REVENGE

There's one thing I haven't said in my story because I don't want you to take it the wrong way. To make sure you hear my heart, let me preface it by saying everything I did, when I listened to the serpent, when I believed his lie, when I ate the fruit, when I gave it to Adam, all of that was absolutely in my hands to do. My next few statements aren't in any way intended to mitigate my responsibility in allowing sin into Elohim's perfect world and causing the fall of man. I hope you get that because what happened that day in the Garden is the serpent stole creation.

He stole it. I was the means by which he achieved his thievery, I was his unwitting accomplice, but the bottom line is he stole it. He stole sanctuary. He stole security, purpose, and confidence. He stole love, peace, and joy. All of those things the serpent stole in an instant with the crunching of that fruit. The most significant thing he stole was intimacy and relationship, because when the serpent stole intimacy and relationship, he didn't steal it only from Adam and me, he stole it from you—and he stole it from Yahweh.

Yahweh's love for us is literally incomprehensible. You can stretch your mind and your emotions to their utmost and still not come close to understanding its height, breadth, length, and depth. How many volumes of exposition and innumerable notes of music have been employed attempting to somehow quantify and express His great and inexplicable love for mankind! We keep trying, and I suppose always will. The bottom line is you simply can't. As unspeakably painful as my loss of intimacy with Yahweh was that day in the Garden, the loss He experienced was incalculably greater.

VIRTUOUS VENGEANCE

You've probably suffered an injustice of some kind at some time in your life, so you know your world can feel off-kilter until some sort of retribution has been administered. There's nothing wrong with that feeling. Yahweh's own laws demand penalty for transgression. What is wrong is trying to exact revenge.

Yahweh declares "Vengeance is Mine, and retribution."[8] Usually the word "vengeance" has a negative, even ominous ring. That's because if not meted out in righteousness, vengeance can be vindictive or malicious; probably the reason Yahweh wants us to leave revenge to Him.

Vengeance in the hands of a righteous Judge rights wrongs and restores justice. Righteousness and justice are the very foundation of Yahweh's throne.[9] He's the only One qualified to administer vengeance, and His vengeance is always virtuous.

If you really want to begin to understand Yahweh's great love for you, look again at His words in the Garden when He prophetically declared the serpent's demise.

> *"And I will put enmity between you and the woman, and between your offspring and hers; He will crush your head, and you will strike His heel."*

At that moment, Yahweh set up His greatest revenge. The essence of the word "vengeance" is getting something back. The serpent had stolen the object of His greatest love, but looking down at that hissing, lying snake, Yahweh served notice, "You stole them, but I'm going to get them back."

What it took for Yahweh to get you back is the greatest sacrifice imaginable. The only One qualified to crush the head of the serpent and redeem Elohim's creation, was His Son, Jesus. The only way to destroy sin and its consequences for all time was for it to be crucified, and only One who was without sin could carry the sin of all creation to its death on a cross. It had to be Jesus. There was no other way.

Jesus, my seventy-sixth generation grandson, came to earth through the line of Seth, the son of my Begin Again. Because Adam and I didn't get lost in grief but moved on—twice—a way was made for the Redeemer, for *your* Redeemer to come and fulfill Yahweh's ultimate plan of redemption.

Looking at Adam and me in our wretched half-nakedness before we left the Garden, it was, as always, Yahweh's goodness that triumphed: "I know you were trying to cover up, but I've got something better for you. How about I protect you instead? I know you're trying to defend yourself. How about I be your fortress? I know you're trying to pretend nothing happened. Oh, child, something happened, but it's okay. I'm going to set things right. I'm going to get you back. I'm going to get you *all* back."

And He did!

CONCLUSION
EAT FROM THE TREE OF LIFE

I know the love of Yahweh through the countless ways He blessed me in the Garden, through what I experienced of His immeasurable mercy on Adam and me when we sinned, and His never-ending goodness in our life outside His paradise. As you read my story, I hope you came to know my Elohim better and want to know Him even more fully.

I have one last thing to share before we close these pages, and it's about the Trees. There were two Trees in the Garden—well, there were thousands of trees in the Garden, but only two had names: the Tree of the Knowledge of Good and Evil (from which I infamously ate) and the Tree of Life. Elohim set the Tree of Life in the middle of the Garden (Gen. 2:9) as the centerpiece of His creation because it represents the fullness of life He wants for you. From the beginning, life has been His plan for you. It's still His plan. It will always be His plan.

Just before Yahweh put Adam and me outside the Garden gate, He revealed the importance of the Tree of Life in His plan to get us back from the serpent, and in doing so, once again revealed His immeasurable love for us. It's in your Bible at Genesis 3:22–23.

> *"The man has now become like one of us, knowing good and evil. He must not be allowed to reach out his hand and take also from the tree of life and eat, and live forever. So Yahweh banished him from the Garden of Eden to work the ground from which he had been taken. After he drove the man out, he placed on the east side of the Garden of Eden cherubim and a flaming sword flashing back and forth to guard the way to the Tree of Life."*

The three little words "so Yahweh banished" compose a tiny phrase that reveals a colossal truth about Yahweh. Yahweh didn't send us out of the Garden because He was mad at us for our sin. He wasn't punishing us by taking away our beautiful home. He wasn't an angry father throwing a wayward child out on the street. He was (still is) a loving, compassionate, heartbroken Father protecting His children from eternal separation from Him.

The reason He sent us from the Garden was to keep us from eating of the Tree of Life, becoming trapped in our fallen state, thereby separated from Him forever.

Had we eaten of the Tree of Life before the completion of Yahweh's plan of salvation there would've been no possibility of Jesus, no possibility of redemption, no possibility of getting us back, of getting *you* back.

Yahweh didn't set a fiery-sword-wielding angel to guard the Tree of Life because He wanted to keep us from something good, something more. You know who tells that lie. Yahweh expelled us from the Garden because of His goodness, His love for us, and His compelling desire to walk with us in the cool of the day once again. That's how much He loves us, how much He loves *you*.

Jesus is Yahweh's promised Redeemer, the One He spoke of in the Garden who would one day undo all I had done. He came to give you the life Yahweh has always wanted you to have. Jesus said "The thief comes to kill, steal, and destroy, but I have come that they might have life, and have it abundantly!" (John 10:10). Jesus didn't come to Earth so you can keep breathing. That's not the life to which He's referring.

The word "life" in that verse in your Bible is the Greek word *zoe*, which means "life-life," continuous life[10]. And yes, He's talking about eternity; He's also talking about the quality of life that is yours to grab with both hands, dive into head first, and enjoy (yes, enjoy!). It's a chocolate-batter-covered-bowl life, and it's yours for the licking!

Jesus got back for you the life I lost in the Garden, a life above and beyond all you anticipate or expect[11]. It's a life without limits! It's the Tree-of-Life life, dive-in-head-first-and-devour-every-morsel life! That's the life for which you were designed; the life Jesus won for you when He crushed the serpent's head at Calvary; the life Yahweh invites you to.

Nothing you've done can disqualify you from accepting Yahweh's invitation. It's an invitation to the life-life that's yours when you believe His plan of redemption, as completed by the death and resurrection of Jesus, includes you and nullifies the sin that separated you from Him. My sin, as great as it was, didn't exclude me from Yahweh's plan of redemption. In fact, redemption literally came through me, not in spite of me. Yahweh didn't brush me aside as "sinner"; He won't do that to you either.

Yahweh never disqualifies the sinner. Through Jesus, He opens the gate to the Garden, orders the cherubim to drop their flashy swords, and invites you to eat of the Tree of Life and walk with Him forever. If you've never accepted Yahweh's invitation to redemption and the life-life Jesus offers, take a moment and listen for His voice. It's that inaudible yet undeniable calm, kind, peace-evoking voice you hear at your core. If you hear Him inviting you to walk with Him in the Garden, say "Yes."

Jesus finished the plan. It's done. All that's left is for you to accept His invitation.

Endnotes

1 *The Real Meaning of the Term Helpmeet,* Retrieved at http://www.womeninthescriptures.com/2010/11/real-meaning-of-term-help-meet.html (Sept. 2016).

2 Genesis 1:26 (NIV).

3 Genesis 1:25.

4 Genesis 3:15 (NIV).

5 Isaiah 61:3, Douay-Rheims Bible.

6 *Baca* in many translations. The spelling *Baka* is used here for ease of pronunciation.

7 Ecclesiastes 3:1–4 (NIV).

8 Deuteronomy 32:35 (NASB).

9 Psalm 89:14 (NKJV).

10 *Strong's Greek Concordance,* Retrieved at http://biblehub.com/greek/2222.htm (Sept. 2016).

11 *Strong's Greek Concordance,* Retrieved at http://biblehub.com/greek/4053.htm (Sept. 2016).

CONNECT WITH PAIGE

Paige has been a Bible teacher and speaker for well over 20 years. Although the Genesis Girls series has been a favorite over the years, Paige's favorite thing is simply the Bible. The Word and words of God are the fuel of her life. She doesn't come to bring "Her Thing," her desire is to come alongside whomever shepherds the people—to surround and protect, give aid and relief to that body of believers and their leadership. She brings clear understanding and revelation of Scripture through well-studied messages delivered with humor and real, clear application.

Contact her for retreats, conferences or special events.
paige.henderson@fellowshipofthesword.com

FURTHER CONNECTION

Paige and her husband Richard co-founded Fellowship of the Sword Ministries in 2003. Through week-long retreat-styled encounters, men and women can be reset and restored, discipled and encouraged in very real and relevant ways in relationship to a very real and relevant God.

About Fellowship of the Sword

The Vision is to see people live life free.

The Mission is to lead people in uncovering truth, unlocking identity and unleashing passion.

Fellowship of the Sword serves the Church by facilitating catalytic encounters with God for the purpose of making disciples:

Now without faith it is impossible to please God, for the one who draws near to Him [the catalytic encounter], *must believe that He exists and rewards those who seek Him* [the 2 bedrock principles of discipleship].   Hebrews 11:6

Initial events are the Quest for men and the HeartQuest for women, and they occur—one of each—every month. As of this publication, the ministry has venues in Texas, Missouri, Georgia, England and Bulgaria. To discover more about the ministry (Please do!) or to register for an event (A great idea!) go to www.fellowshipofthesword.com. An excellent and gifted Somebody will get in touch with you to answer any questions you may have or assist you in the registration process.

27836411R00065

Made in the USA
Columbia, SC
01 October 2018